I Like Cam!

Written by C. McCarthy
Illustrated by John Magine

Scott Foresman

I am Cam.

The cat is Mac.

I am Sam.

I like Cam.

I like Mac the cat.

 I like the car.

It is red.

I like the bus.

The bus is yellow.

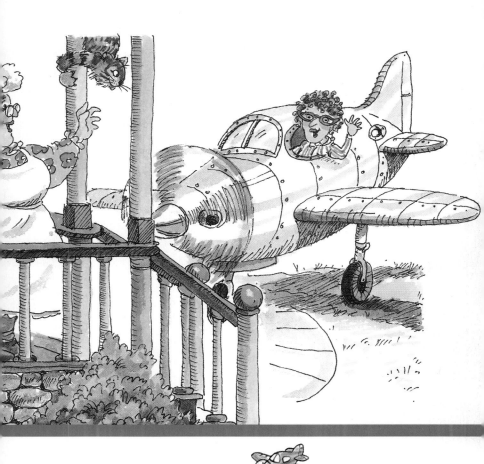

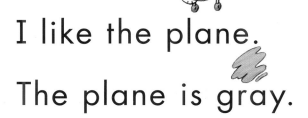 I like the plane.

The plane is gray.

I like Cam.

I like Mac the brown cat.

I like cookies.